RADIO TIMES BRAINBOX
PUZZLE BOOK

BY CLIVE DOIG

BBC BOOKS

for Natasha

The author would like to thank the following for
their help in the preparation of this book:
Julie Allan, John Collis, John Davies, Julia Doig,
Julian Flanders, Rachel Hardman, Sarah
Spalding and Sian Rees.

Cover illustration and cartoons on pages 16, 19,
21, 25 and 38 by Brian Robins
Diagrams by Mike Gilkes

Published by BBC Books,
a division of BBC Enterprises Limited,
Woodlands, 80 Wood Lane, London W12 0TT
First Published 1989

ISBN 0 563 20801 5

Set in 10 on 11 pt Plantin by Ace Filmsetting Ltd, Frome, Somerset
Printed and bound in Great Britain by Redwood Press Ltd, Trowbridge, Wiltshire
Cover printed by Richard Clay Ltd, Norwich

CONTENTS

Introduction   6

How to Score   7

Puzzles   8

Answers at a Glance   45

Full Solutions   49

Trackword Answers   69

INTRODUCTION

My Brainbox puzzles have been running along with TRACKWORDS in the *Radio Times* since 1980.

I have always attempted to make up puzzles that are easily solved using logical thought or a limited general knowledge of words and numbers. The 'mindbogglingness' of some of them usually relates to the reader's own willingness to spend time, with pencil and paper, trying out various routes of logic and trial and error. Wherever possible the conundrums and brainteasers do not require a great amount of acquired knowledge.

It is very easy to compile really difficult puzzles simply by writing them in impossible codes or making references to obscure scientific principles or languages. A simple sequence, like 1 3 6 7 2 9 4 8 5, that has an answer such as 'the order of the numbers is alphabetical in Hungarian (*Egy, Harom, Hat, Het, Ket, Kilenc, Negy, Nyolc, Ot*)' is easy to compile and solve, especially if you are a Hungarian, but pretty unfair for the average non-Hungarian speaking *Radio Times* reader. Nowhere in this book do I ever refer to Hungarian again nor indeed to any other language other than English. Higher calculus, Fibonacci numbers and the Mandelbrot sets are for higher intellects. Simple algebra, geometry and logic are the only tools of Maths you will ever really need.

The principle of solving problems with a Matrix grid has been used for many of the full solutions in the back of the book.

In the *Radio Times* we never have the space either to print the whole solution or the deduction process leading to the simple answer, nor to print the full list of words that can be tracked through TRACKWORD. This book gives me the opportunity to do both, and so reply to all my critical correspondents who have doubted both the answers and the average and brainbox TRACKWORD scores.

HOW TO SCORE

For those who wish to score, the questions carry 3 points for each answer in whole or in part.

Each question has either one answer or is divided into parts. For each separate answer required score 3 points. Reaching the average number of words in a TRACKWORD is worth 3 points.

Wherever you fail to achieve the correct answer or cheat by looking it up or come up with an answer that is entirely different, then mark yourself honestly on a scale down from 3 to 0. If you believe the answer is wrong and can prove an alternative or different solution write to me at the *Radio Times* and I will personally award you 3 points.

QUESTION FOR SCORERS

Question 178: – Giving 3 points to each and every part of all 178 questions in this book, as described above, what is the total score possible?

RESULTS

Having completed all the questions or not; the following deductions of your ability can be made:

700+ pts You are a genius or you are one of my relations or possibly you are me.

500–700 An intelligent puzzle-solver and regular *Radio Times* reader.

400–500 A very high mark, shows that you've at least attempted every question or simply cannot add up.

200–400 This is highly average, means that you could have a career as a politician or a prime minister one day.

100–200 Pretty poor achievement, but does suggest you too could turn to compiling your own puzzles.

15–100 Luckily this is not the worst result attainable but probably means you hate doing puzzles.

1–15 Is a category of total dumbness, illiteracy or apathy, probably means you were given the book for Christmas and have since only used it to prop up the kitchen table or as cat litter.

0 Probably means that you have never looked beyond this page or that you are a native Serbo-Croat or that you have had the book confiscated by a teacher, vicar or boss, or that you haven't bothered with scoring or you haven't actually got the book.

PUZZLES

1 HANDFUL

Six cards are shown here

Hand 1

Colour key for cards

RED   YELLOW   GREEN   BLUE   BLACK

Here are the same six cards shuffled around –
some have been turned over

Hand 2

And the same six cards again

Hand 3

Only one of the cards has the same colour back as its suit. Which one?

2 COLOUR IN

If you coloured in the sections of the diagram below with just four colours
so that no two sections that lie next to each other are the same colour,
which of Sections A or B has to be the same colour as section C?

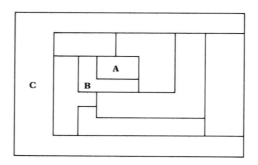

3 ZOO STORY

Can you find 25 different mammals, three birds, one fish and one insect hidden in the story below?

> Erica the rhinoceros wanted to do good, but she couldn't. Neither could she bear being locked up in her box, and would rather have escaped. However, she was so hungry that she lifted a sign up, ignored the fact that it said 'Do not feed', and ate it! Her scowling keeper came later, saw the chewed sign, and, knowing she episodically ate strange things, made Erica a feed of best oats. 'I want eaters of oats and grass, not notice boards,' he said shrewdly. Erica stamped the floor angrily, as if to say, 'So what?' The keeper relented. 'OK, a piece of nice batter pudding then.' Erica thankfully wolfed the pudding of batter down.

CAT
ANT
DOG
PIG
LING
COW
DEER
STOAT
ANTEATER
ASS
BOAR
WOLF

4 MONTHS

J&R

My first begins most months
My second occurs most in all the months
My third occurs in most months
My last two letters end most months equally.

Who am I?

5 CHOCOLATE DROPS

You have 20 tubes of chocolate drops; each tube contains 20 identical sweets. You are told that all the tubes weigh exactly 100 grams except one which weighs only 80 grams, though you cannot tell by looking. You have a weighing machine that accurately shows you the weight to the nearest gram.

What is the least number of weighings you need to do to identify which tube is the lighter one?

6 MANY BEARS

Starting with SUPERTED, read through the grid, up, down or across, to find another 11 well-known bears.

```
Y  S  U  P  E  R  T  E  D  R
T  O  O  E  H  I  N  B  E  U
E  D  S  P  T  E  N  E  H  P
T  E  L  O  B  O  I  A  T  E
I  G  T  O  O  W  R  T  R  R
B  T  T  H  O  G  O  Y  B  A
Y  E  I  P  B  I  N  G  N  L
E  D  L  A  D  D  I  T  O  O
N  R  A  B  O  F  F  I  B  O
```

7 MOVE AROUND

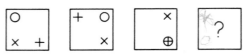

Which of the squares below comes next in the sequence above?

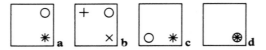

8 STRANGE TALE

In the story below 23 letters of the alphabet have been doubled up in words (one more than once).
Three letters are not doubled up.
Which are they?

An aardwolf and a rabbit decided to go skiing together in the snow.
'Aha!' said the bunny, 'This slope looks nice and slippery.'
The wolf withheld his fear and after a short powwow with his friend agreed. They both whizzed off down the slope paw in paw, but the furry bun unfortunately tripped up and brought the bigger animal down. They both slid to the bottom on their tummies and landed on top of a carduus
– a type of thistle – which was hidden in the snow.
'Oh bovver!' said the bun, 'We're covered in prickles and trapped.'
Luckily a passing trekker, who was on a hajj (pilgrimage) to Mecca, picked them up out of the prickly drift, and they lived happily ever after to tell the tale.

9 SWAP FIVE

The five letters of one word have been swapped for five letters of another word throughout the sentence below.

What are the two words?

YLE FIVE GOBGYIYOYEG CAR BE DEDOCED WIYLIR YLIG
GERYERCE WLICL LAGR'Y OGED YLEM IR IY

TRACKWORDS

How many words of three letters or more can you find by tracking from one square to the next; going up, down, sideways or diagonally in order?

You may not go through the same letter square again in one word.
No plurals (with an added s), proper nouns or foreign words are allowed.

What is the nine-letter word that can be extracted by tracking through all the letters of the grid?

10

M	E	R
E	A	D
R	I	N

Average score: 43 words
Brainbox score: 79 words

11

H	T	W
O	O	R
U	T	G

Average score: 26 words
Brainbox score: 41 words

12

L	N	I
E	A	K
T	I	C

Average score: 30 words
Brainbox score: 51 words

NUMBERS AND LETTERS

What expressions, phrases or sayings are represented by these numbers and letters? A number stands for a number, a capital letter is the initial letter of a word.

13 3 G in a H T

14 8 L of an O

15 1 2 B M S

16 The P M L at 10 D S

17 A 4 M M

18 8 F in a M

19 6 P on a S T

20 1 2 3 4 5 O I C a F A

21 A the W in 80 D

22 3 P for a W, 1 for a D

23 **GHOSTS**

The one who is scary is not squarey
The stripey ghost is a girl
Spooky Luke is not next to Eve
Scary Mary is next to the dotty ghost
Creepy Crispin is the brother of Eerie Eve

Who is who?

24   DOCTOR WHO

Here are two well-known adversaries of Doctor Who drawn with the letters of their names. Each adversary has one letter missing.

What do the missing letters represent?

25   FOOTBALL POINTS

On Bank Holiday there were 11 matches played in the English Football League Second Division, which were all on the Pools coupon.
Strangely the total number of points for wins (3 pts) and draws (1 pt) gained by the Second Division teams overall was exactly equal to the total points derived from their results on the pools coupon (i.e. 3 pts for a score draw, 2 pts for a no-score draw, 1½ pts for an away win and 1 pt for a home win).

How many score draws were there in the division if there were no no-score draws?

26   QUEENIE

In chess the queen can move any number of squares in a horizontal, vertical or diagonal line. This gives her a total of 1456 possible legitimate moves.

How many legitimate moves does she have moving anywhere on the board to and from squares of the same colour?

27   TENNIS

If 110 ladies are in the draw for a tennis doubles knock-out championship, how many matches will be played altogether to complete the tournament?

28 WEIGHINGS

You have twelve bars of chocolate, one of which is lighter or heavier than the others. You have only one balance and no weights. What is the least number of weighings you need to identify the lighter or heavier bar, and indicate which it is.

TRACKWORDS

How many words of three letters or more can you find by tracking from one square to the next; going up, down, sideways or diagonally in order?

What is the nine-letter word that can be extracted by tracking through all the letters of the grid?

29

C	E	T
T	O	A
O	R	D

Average score: 32 words
Brainbox score: 55 words

30

N	I	P
E	A	P
H	S	S

Average score: 22 words
Brainbox score: 38 words

31

E	S	T
N	I	E
G	A	M

Average score: 37 words
Brainbox score: 66 words

32 FLAGS

Which national flag is the odd one out?
UK, USA, France, Costa Rica, Czechoslovakia, Dominican Republic, Iceland, Sweden, Thailand.

33 BRITISH RIVERS

Work out what the six mixed-up British rivers are below.

Take their first letters, juggle them around, and make a seventh British river.

NOVA   OLME   WHYTSTY   TWENDER   KES   RAWE

AVON MOLE   DERWENT EST WEAR

34 MORE RIVERS

Do the same thing again, this time travelling the world.

GNOMEK   ZAMAON   NEVERS   SHUNDO   STREEL   STIRGI

AMAZON   SEVERN

35 ER

Whrer I erad e I srr r and whrer I erad r I srr e.
If I srr thr woed crerbeal what should it erally br?

36 FRACTIONAL SPEECH

Can you make sense of the following sentence?

$$\frac{STAND}{I} \quad TE(U)ND \quad \frac{PAY}{2} \quad \frac{MY}{TIME} \quad \frac{TAKER'S}{4} \quad WORK$$

37 SCHOOL ROOMS

The picture above shows a school block. There are 18 similar sized class-rooms in this one building, nine at the front and nine at the back, which you cannot see. The classrooms are numbered in a logical sequence. The Gymnasium is Room 1.

Room 14 is the Geography Room.
The Chemistry Lab is opposite Room 12.
The Music Room is opposite the Art Room.

What number is the Music Room?

38 FIRST AND LAST

Take the first and last letters of the five things below and juggle them around to find out where you can look for more.

IORRFG
ARPE

39 MY FAT FRIEND

Read the following carefully:

MY DPY CH HPHREY KÖHLER, WITH AN LAUT, LIVES IN HBERSIDE WITH HIS JBO M. HIS HOUSE IS A BIT OF A SL, BUT HE DOESN'T GRBLE – HE'S NEVER GRPY OR GL. HE'S ALWAYS CONSING NEROUS SCRPTIOUS THINGS, SUCH AS SATSAS, KQUATS AND PPKINS, PL CRBLE, R DPLINGS AND PTEEN CRPETS; HE'S ALSO ALWAYS CHEWING LPY G OR HBUGS. AS YOU CAN ASSE, HIS TMY IS VOLINOUSLY PLP AND I THINK HE'S A BIT OF A CHP.
BUT ENOUGH OF THIS BUNK ABOUT THE TRAAS OF HPHREY'S DIET. LET'S GET TO THE HDR POINT OF THIS CONUNDR.
WHAT IS THE MAXIM NBER OF MISSING S IN THIS HBLE TALE?

40 SWEETS

I had some sweets, my friend ate half of them, I had one. Then my friend ate half the remainder and I ate the last one. 6

How many more sweets did my friend have than me? 4

16

41 TENNIS TOURNAMENT

In a tennis tournament consisting of ladies' and men's singles and mixed-doubles in which everyone played, only three people got to the finals without losing a match.

Is this possible?

TRACKWORDS

How many words of three letters or more can you find?

42

O	G	S
L	I	T
O	O	Z

Average score: 12 words
Brainbox score: 20 words

43

L	A	S
G	O	T
N	I	C

Average score: 46 words
Brainbox score: 82 words

44

E	M	U
R	A	N
C	I	L

Average score: 28 words
Brainbox score: 48 words

EXPRESSIBLES

What are the expressions or phrases represented by these diagrams?

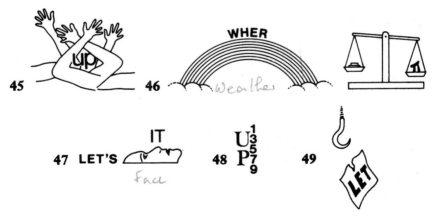

45

46 WHER
Weather

47 LET'S IT
Face

48 U¹³⁵⁷⁹P
$U^1_3{}^5_7{}_9 P$

49 LET

17

50 PHONEUMBLE

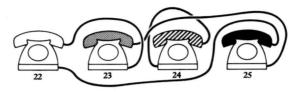

Here are four office extension phones, but some clever dick has put the handsets down on the wrong bases.

If extension 22 was to ring, which of the handsets would you need to pick up to answer the call?   25

51 POURINGS

5 LITRES   3 LITRES   20 LITRES

The two buckets above are full of precious liquid.

How many pourings, using only the buckets and the container on the right, do you need to measure out exactly 4 litres of liquid without throwing away a drop?

52 TOWERS

RED
GREEN
YELLOW
GREEN
RED

YELLOW
RED
GREEN
RED
YELLOW

The five rings on the left are 5, 10, 15, 20 and 25 cms in diameter. The five rings on the right are 2, 4, 6, 8 and 10 ins in diameter.

How many different towers of five rings can you make so that they decrease in size from bottom to top and so that rings of the same colour are not next to each other?   5.8 , 11.6 , 17.4 , 23.2 , 25.4

(NB: 1 in is approximately 2.54 cms)

18

53 THE QUEUE

The six ladies waiting at the bus stop have the same initials to their Christian names as to their surnames.

Olga Oojit wears a red hat.

Ms Igglend and Ms Faskie are both facing the same way.

Harriet Howzyafather can see three other ladies with hats.

When she arrived Fanny pushed into the queue.

Ms Sploknorst hates the colour blue.

The lady immediately on Ms Armbustrage's right owns a dog called Nelson.

Ivy is two places ahead of Annie.

Sue has just eaten her lunch.

Who is who?

54 DIE IN THE MIRROR

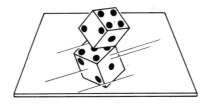

Here is one die supported so that only one corner touches a mirror. We can see four of its faces.

What is wrong with the mirror image?

What is the maximum number of faces of a die you could see, given that some part of it has to touch a mirror?

TRACKWORDS

How many words of three letters or more can you find?

55

R	T	L
E	A	E
H	S	S

Average score: 52 words
Brainbox score: 85 words

56

Y	R	L
E	A	P
X	E	M

Average score: 38 words
Brainbox score: 64 words

57

S	E	N
T	A	D
R	E	E

Average score: 58 words
Brainbox score: 103 words

58 ANIMALS

Each of the animals below has one letter replaced by another. If you write down the letters that have been replaced you will spell out another animal. What is it?

NOW   BARE   PEG   ACE   LOOSE   BELL   SKULK   YAM

59 MINIMUM WORDS

Can you make four, four-letter English words using all the first 16 letters of the alphabet?

A B C D E F G H I J K L M N O P

MILK
BANG

60 ENDPART

WHICH SINGLE
What part of the body can you add to each of the following to make a word?

F . . .   C . . .   S . . .   TU . . .   COWS . . .

61 TABLE

Who is missing?

RIO GRANGE HORSE
STRING ROAR
UNTREACLY CAMP

20

62 OOPS

?Ecnetnes siht ni yltcerroc sdrawkcab nettirw ton si drow tahW

63 SECRET LETTERS

Follow the story carefully:

THIS IS A PICTURE OF A SECRET GARDE GUARDED BY A
ASTY GOME WHO HAS STOLE A LETTER FROM IT. HE WO'T
LET AYBODY I ULESS THEY KOW THE LETTER.
TWO CHILDRE CALLED ORA AD ICK KOW THE MISSIG LET-
TER. 'IT IS   ,' SAID ICK. 'OW CA WE PICK SOME RUER BEAS
FOR OUR DIER?'
'O!' GRIED THE GOME, SCRATCHIG HIS LOG OSE. 'I HERE
YOU CA OLY PICK ASTURTIUMS, AEMOES AD PEOIES.'
'AD OSES, BY THE LOOK OF YOU,' ORA SIGGERED.
'THAT'S UFAIR,' ICK SARLED, 'WE WAT RUER BEAS WITH
OUR JOIT.'
'OH! ALL RIGHT THE,' THE GOME SIFFED, AD WIKED WICK-
EDLY. 'IF YOU CA COUT UP THE EXACT UMBER OF MISSIG
  S I THIS STORY, YOU CA PICK WHATEVER YOU WAT.'
'THAK YOU,' THEY SAID, AD THEY DID. SO THEY GOT THEIR
RUER BEAS FOR THEIR DIER.

What is the total?

64 PIANO KEYS

BCDEFGABCDEF

I have a piano which goes from a G in the bass to a C in the treble and has eight A's altogether.

How many notes are there on my piano?

NUMBERS AND LETTERS

What expressions, phrases or sayings are represented by these numbers and letters. A number stands for a number, a capital letter is the initial letter of a word.

65 2's C, 3's a C

66 240 O P in a P *Old Pence in a Pound*

67 76 T in the B P *Trombones Big Parade*

68 S W and the 7 D

69 8 P in a G *Pints Gallon*

70 2 L B E

71 26 L of the A *Letters Alphabet.*

72 15 M in a R U T

73 20000 L U the S

74 6 F in a F

75 12 S of the Z *Signs Zodiac*

76 9 P of the S S

77 6 C in S of an A

78 12 P on a J

79 5 L of a S

22

80 1 M W to M

81 W 3 K of O A

82 S G the K of the D N B 21 B

83 The 6 W of H 8

84 A of 1000 D

85 ALPHABETICAL NAMES

How many Christian names can you find which are spelled in alphabetical order?

For example: BERT or GUY

You may use short forms – like 'JO' – and double letters – as in BILLY.

You're doing well if you find 17, and very well if you find 25, any more probably means you know a lot of foreign names.

86 LACITEBAHPLA SEMAN

Now try and find Christian names which are spelled in reverse alphabetical order.

For example: NED

87 RELATIONS

Chris has twice as many brothers as sisters, but Chris's brother Tom has twice as many sisters as brothers.

How many children are there in Chris's family?

88 MORE RELATIONS

John's wife is Bill's elder sister Mary and her elder brother Nick is married to Bill's wife's younger sister Rita. Bill's brother-in-law is Kate's elder brother.

If the ages of the six married people above all lie within two years of each other, which couple has the lowest sum of their ages?

89 TILES

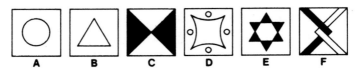

Each of the tiles shown above costs 20p
  or
£1.50 for a packet of eight of the same design
  or
£4 for a packet of 24 of the same design.
All the tiles are 10 cm × 10 cm.

What is the least you would have to pay for tiles, in order to tile a square eight tiles by eight, so that every tile in every line across, up and down or diagonally looked different?
(In this case 'looking different' means that you can turn some of the tiles upside down or on their sides: ie tile 'B' upside down and tile 'C' on its side would be different from 'B' and 'C' as shown above, but tile 'A' is the same whichever way up it goes.)

90 OBJECTIVE

What is the object for which the outline is

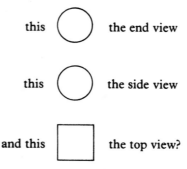

this   the end view

this   the side view

and this   the top view?

91   CHRISTMAS THINGS

Take the third letter of each of the Christmas things below, rearrange them
and make a Christmas entertainment.
(Do not use the word Christmas in front of those marked *.)

92   PANTOMIMES

Solve each of the clues below to find the names of a well-known panto-
mime. (~~The marked letters spell out another one~~.)

   a Answer to 'Christmas Things' (puzzle 90)   _ _ _ _ _ * _ _ _ _

   b Like a frog from a home   _ _ _ _ _ _ _ * _ _ _ _ _ _

a) ✓**c** Two lost infants   _ _ * _ _ _ _ _ _ _ _ _ _ _

b) ✓**d** Mayor of London with cat   _ _ _ _ _ _ _ _ _ _ * _ _ _ _ _

   e Left alone, but not by Friday   _ _ _ _ _ _ _ * _ _ _ _ _ _

   f A reconstituted egg   * _ _ _ _ _ _ _ _ _ _ _

c) ✓**g** A gosling's mum   _ * _ _ _ _ _ _ _ _ _

d) ✓**h** A cat in the chemists   _ _ _ _ _ _ _ _ * _ _

   i The boy and a big vegetable   _ _ _ _ _ _ * _ _ _ _

   _ _ _ _ _ _ _ _ _

25

93 OVER TO YOU

What have all the different answers to these questions got in common?

a German Mrs ....

b African humped ox ....

c Indian language ....

d French goodbye ....

e Shortened viral infection ....

f Flightless bird ....

g Bill of fare ....

h Wildebeest ....

i Not me ....

j Without preparation ....

TRACKWORDS

How many words of three letters or more can you find?

94

M	E	S
R	A	T
C	E	R

Average score: 70 words
Brainbox score: 120 words

95

C	H	T
E	A	L
D	N	O

Average score: 40 words
Brainbox score: 72 words

96

S	C	R
M	A	E
B	L	D

Average score: 66 words
Brainbox score: 115 words

EXPRESSIBLES

What are the expressions or phrases represented by these diagrams?

97 WILL WAY

100 IN L OUT

98 GIBLSSSNE

101 ADO ADOADO ADO ADO ADO ADO ADO ADO ADO ADO ADOADO ADO

99 ONCE
12·55

102 FOUR CARDS

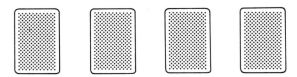

Here are four playing cards of different suits which have consecutive values.
The club is to the left of the heart.
The 8 of spades is next to the card which is immediately to the right of the club.
The 7 of hearts is two away from the card which is between the two highest cards.

What value is the diamond and where is it?

103 TRADESMEN

Five tradesmen live in a row of five houses next to each other.
None of them has the same name as their own trade.
The baker lives next to the grocer.
The Smiths (Mr Smith and the smith) live at either end of the row.
Looking at the row of houses, Mr Grocer lives three doors away from
Mr Turner.
The butcher lives in the middle house.

What is Mr Baker's trade?

104 ANIMALS

What are these animals and what order are they in?

GION, CHTAH, GIRAE, AMA, LEING, BABN, FEET,
OPOUM, POO

105 BIRDS

Put these birds into the same order as in puzzle 104.

CUCK, PUIN, PWIT, NOY, GAET, HOY, BIERN, PAOT,
SWAOW, DIER

106 MASTERWORD

Take the letter in each word that does not occur in any other word
and jumble them around to get another five-letter word.

COAST, TIRED, YACHT, MIRTH, STAND

What is the word?

107 ROW

Six children are standing in a row. A girl does not stand next to a boy
and a boy does not stand next to another boy.

How is that possible?

TRACKWORDS

How many words of three letters or more can you find?

108

P	R	E
O	A	D
M	E	N

Average score: 45 words
Brainbox score: 85 words

109

R	D	D
A	O	E
W	R	F

Average score: 34 words
Brainbox score: 56 words

110

M	F	R
U	A	E
L	S	T

Average score: 54 words
Brainbox score: 88 words

111   7 W WORDS

Can you find the seven, seven-letter words which have the following three consonants appearing consecutively in them?

WKW, WDL, WSL, WDR, WST, WSB, WTH

112   DUOS

Can you pair up the mixed-up names below?

Which pair is the odd one out?

LAURY   COSTOTT   LITGE   DISTONE   ALTORIA   HARDEL
MORESE   VICBERT   GLADSRAELL   BON   ABBELLO   WICAMBE
CANNALL   LARTLE   FLANEN   ALLAGAN

113   PANDA STORY

A sheep and a panda were cooking bamboo shoots in a saucepan. Daisy the sheep, read out the instructions on the tin to Panda: 'Make the pan damp and apply heat; the shoots will expand at once'.

How many pandas are there in the story?

114 NAMES

Which two names in the sequence below do not follow the rule applied to the others?

PATRICIALANNAOMIKEITHELMARTINGRIDAVID

115 LINES

Six straight lines are needed to join each point to every other point above.

How many straight lines are needed to join each point to every other point below?

. . .

. . .

. . .

116 TRIANGLES

When you have drawn and counted all the lines above, work this out:

What is the total number of triangles that appear in the pattern?

117 CUBES

The six faces of a cube can be represented by a diagram like the one below.
Point 'A' joins point 'A' and the two side pieces flap down to make a cube.

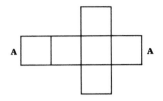

Here are two drawings of the same cube from different angles.

Which of the exploded drawings below represents the cube above?

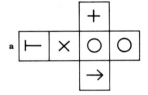   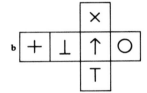

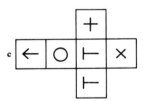   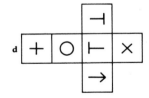

31

118 SEVEN BITS

Each of the seven answers to the clues below has a bit in them.

a A bird that isn't sweet to the North

b Mostly a Jewish furry animal

c What the moon and the earth are in

d An old measure

e What one needs to be successful

f Not credit

g Display or show

The first letters of each answer spell another word. What is it?

119 LETTER AWAY

Start with something dirty
TAKE A LETTER AWAY, mix up, get a ball game
TAKE A LETTER AWAY, get a jewel
TAKE A LETTER AWAY, mix up, get a word meaning to purchase
TAKE A LETTER AWAY, get by

120 KEYWORD

My keyword has five letters: 12345

1235 is like a stalk
5412 is like a pole
5342 is what some people eat
3412 is a direction
1345 is a join in cloth

What is my keyword?

TRACKWORDS

How many words of three letters or more can you find?

121

W	E	N
S	E	R
P	A	P

Average score: 41 words
Brainbox score: 71 words

122

D	E	J
T	U	I
S	I	F

Average score: 14 words
Brainbox score: 24 words

123

P	Y	E
H	O	T
C	R	I

Average score: 26 words
Brainbox score: 42 words

EXPRESSIBLES

What are the expressions or phrases represented by these diagrams?

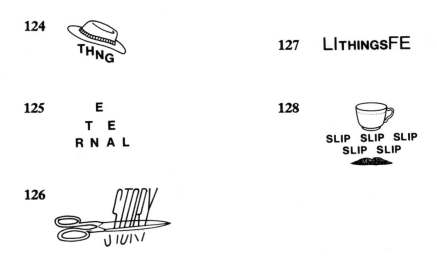

124

THNG

127 LIthingsFE

125

E
T E
R N A L

128

SLIP SLIP SLIP
SLIP SLIP

126

STORY

129 LETTERED CARDS

Here are three cards with different letters on both sides.

Here are the same three cards in different positions.
Two of them have been turned over.

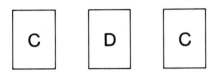

Here are the three cards in different positions again and once more two of them have been turned over. An ink blot obscures one of them.

Which letter is it?

EXPRESSIBLES

What are the expressions or phrases represented by these diagrams?

130 BEBUSHAT

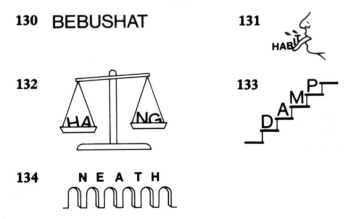

131

132

133

134 N E A T H

135 FRUITCAKE

If a FRUITCAKE = 18
a SLIMYTHING = 24
and a BULLDOZER = 30,

What does:
'A fruitcake and a half, plus half a half a slimything, less a half and half a bulldozer' equal in fruitcakes?

136 KCAB

?ECNETNES SIHT NI SDRAWKCAB DELLEPS YLREPORP TN'SI DROW TAHW

137 VOWELS

As you cao see, a fault has developed oo this typewriter. Ooe letter always comes out as aoother.

What are the words below aod which ooe has the most oumber of coosecutive vowels io it?

SPOOTAOEOUS IOGEOUOUS MOOOTOOOUS
MOUOTAIOOUS OOIOOS CAOOOO CAOOEIOG QUEUIOG
QUIOIOE IOAOE AOOIAO PROOOUO TRUOOIOO

138 OOE TO FIVE

Iosert plusses or miouses aoywhere **betweeo** these oumbers to make the sum correct.
You cao ooly use + or − sigos.

$$1 \ 2 \ 3 \ 4 \ 5 = 12$$

How maoy solutioos are there?

139 LAUGHS

Thank goodness the typewriter is now mended.

Can you find five mirthful words reading from left to right through the letters below, using each letter only once?

LAGGITHOGRIOGLITTUNGEERTH

140 MORE LAUGHS

Find another word like snigger or smile by taking the first letter of the first word in this sentence which is similar to snicker, the second letter of the second word that is a bit less than a chortle, the third from the third, the fourth from the fourth and the fifth letter from the fifth word which is chuckle.

What merry word do you get?

141 SIBLINGS

There are three children in each of two different families, the Puckeridges and the Shotovers.
The children all married each other. There are now more Puckeridges than Shotovers.
Jacob is Ermintrude's sister's husband.
Su-Ellen has no sisters.
Algernon is married to the sister of Daphne's husband.
Archibald has black hair.

Who married who?

NUMBERS AND LETTERS

What expressions, phrases or sayings are represented by these numbers and letters. A number stands for a number, a capital letter is the initial letter of a word.

142 90 D in a R A

143 1 R and 2 L

144 30 D in A J S and N

145 6 or 8 B in a B

146 C o' 9 T

147 3 M in a B

148 X E 10 in R N

149 5 S of a P

150 12 I in a F

151 16 O in a P

152 212 D F is the B P of W

153 A 4 L C

154 1984 was W by G O

155 F F and 40

156 28 D in F

157 31 D in J and J

158 366 D in a L Y

159 24 H from T

160 3 C in a F

161 60 S in a M

162 BOTOBIAN MONEY

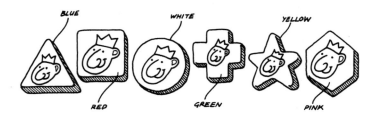

BLUE WHITE YELLOW

RED GREEN PINK

'I'll never get used to the currency of Botobia,' said Alan when he returned from holiday. 'There are 11 gimlips to 1 nogwod, and 3 nogwods to a yat.'
'That's 33 gimlips to the yat,' smiled his girlfriend Sally.
'That's the easy part, just look at the Botobian coins.' Alan showed her the six coins shown above.
'Oh, but they're pretty,' Sally exclaimed.
'Those are only a few of all the Botobian coins as well,' he laughed.
'What are they each worth?' Sally asked.
Alan sighed. 'Well, it depends on the colour. If they're white or yellow then they are gimlips, if they are blue or green then they're nogwods and pink or red means they are yats.'
'Got it so far,' nodded Sally.
'Their shapes show their denomination, how much each one is worth in gimlips, nogwods or yats according to the number of edges they've got.'
'Oh! I see, that's quite simple really,' Sally mused. 'What's the exchange rate?'
'Exactly 1 nogwod 6 gimlips to the pound.'
'If only you had one more coin you'd have exactly £30 worth of Botobian money,' the girl with five degrees in higher mathematics said smartly.

a What shape and colour would that be?

'Smart aren't you,' Alan said a little hurt when she had to tell him.
'I've told you before,' Sally said rather cruelly, 'you will have to do much better at arithmetic before I ever marry you.'
'OK clever dick,' Alan went on, 'but I haven't told you about the norg, have I?' and he produced a further Botobian circular silver coin from his pocket.
'The norg!' Sally exclaimed.
'I worked out that it's the first Botobian coin worth an exact number of pounds.'
'Good heavens that's valuable,' Sally worked out, as quick as lightning.

b How many yats are there in a norg?

'It's a shame you haven't got a dodecagonal silver norg isn't it?', Sally dreamed of the eminent wealth of that coin.

'Oh, but I did bring back half a dozen dodecagon gold zmukkis, do you think they're worth anything?' Alan smiled showing her the six little gold coins he took out of his trouser pocket.

Sally nearly fell over. She gasped and stuttered, 'Tell me gently Alan, how many norgs are there in a zmukki?'

'I think they said it was the same number of gimlips as there are in a norg,' he replied.

Sally's brain ticked over for a few seconds and then she smiled very broadly. 'I think I will marry you after all, Alan.'

c How much in pounds sterling were the six little gold coins worth?

163 GROUPS

What have each of the following groups of numbers got in common? (Think of matches, lines and words)

a 5, 9, 10, 11, 15 etc.

b THREE, FOUR, SIX, NINE, ELEVEN, FIFTY-ONE etc.

c 3, 7, 8, 40, 50, 60 only

d II, III, V, VI, VIII, IX, X etc.

e I, III, V, IX, XII, XXI etc.

f Four, seven, ten, twelve, twenty-four, sixty, sixty, one hundred, one thousand.

g 3, 7, 12, 16, 19, 21, 25, 30, 41, 45, 52 etc.

h 2, 3, 10, 12, 13, 20, 21 etc.

164 MENU

This is the menu at the 'Restarrant Mispel'.
What fruit is used in the dessert?

SEA SOAP

*   *   *

GATE TIE
with
MALE & CHOPS

*   *   *

FLAB

TRACKWORDS

How many words of three letters or more can you find?

165

S	N	G
P	A	I
R	E	D

Average score: 57 words
Brainbox score: 91 words

166

L	E	R
E	A	T
C	H	W

Average score: 56 words
Brainbox score: 96 words

167

E	T	S
R	A	L
R	E	P

Average score: 60 words
Brainbox score: 98 words

168 A AGREEABLE DAY

The same three letters have been carded from the beginning of a number of words in this puzzle. Can you cover them and work out how many times they are missing?

'It was a mal day and I could cern aster in the air as I washed up the gustingly dirty breakfast hes and cussed with my tinctly tressed mother the turbances we had recently had in the trict.
The day before a group of demonstrators showed a lack of cipline while being persed by the police and had trampled across our garden.
The tinguished c jockey who lives next door was puting our rights of way.
Our hevelled dog had got temper.
Dad had lost his job at the tillery, and a tant aunt was coming to stay.
I pelled my traught mother's worst fears and decided to tance myself for a day or two.'

169   ADD A LETTER

Add a letter to each answer to get the answer to the next question:

a First person singular   _

b Opposite of not in   _ _

c The bin in ice-hockey   _ _ _

d To voice a verse   _ _ _ _

e A bee's weapon   _ _ _ _ _

f As long as a piece of   _ _ _ _ _ _

g Fixed looking   _ _ _ _ _ _ _

h A bird   _ _ _ _ _ _ _ _

i Frightening   _ _ _ _ _ _ _ _ _

170   ELEMENTARY

What word is spelt out by the first letters of the chemical elements whose symbols are given below?

NASBHGKPBFENAU

171   BIRTHDAY CARDS

Five friends with the same birthday sat round a round table to give cards to each other.
Although they all received the same number of cards, each gave a different number out, and Joseph did not give any!!
Gertie gave her one card to Harry, but he did not give her one.
Isobel received cards from people sitting either side of her.
Fred gave his cards just to the people sitting either side of him.
Joseph and Harry were sitting next to each other.
Fred received a card from the person sitting immediately on his left.

How were they sitting, and how many cards did each give out?

172   WORD GAMES

If ANNA is to BOB
what is OTTO to ?

If DAD is to DEED
what is PIP to ?

173 CODE

Can you break the code and answer the question? The numbers 0–9 each stand for the same letter throughout.

780 150604 D07017I60 I960970D BY 3I4 A478U4 1O9A9 DOY5O I3, OF 1OU430, 38045O12 8O5M03. W8A7 I3 8I3 A33I37A97'3 9AM0, I9 1OD0?

174 FOOTBALL

Five teams played each other once. Under the old scoring system they scored two points for a win, one for a draw, and none for a loss. The final table looked like this:

Team	Goals for	Goals against	Points
Minty	aa	a	b
Nontown	b	c	d
Oghead	d	e	e
Pester	f	g	h
Queenford	h	i	a

The numbers 1–9 have been substituted by letters.

All the games had different results.
Pester lost to Minty 0–5 and to Nontown 0–3.
Queenford only scored three goals altogether.
Simon Tusker of Oghead was the only player to score a hat trick, and Uriah Valheim of Minty scored in every game.
Wally Ximinax, Minty's goalie only once failed to make a save.

If Nontown and Oghead drew 2–2, what was the score in the Minty v. Queenford match?

175 A CLUE DOIG

Before Miss Scarlet was murdered she made this last telephone call:
'When will this weather ever end, greenhouses are not the place to be with the door open, I shall go elsewhere.'

Who murdered her, with what and where?

176 DIY TRACKWORD

Answer the simple word clues to find the nine letters of the Trackword.

a What item of clothing can you put in front of ABLE, RICE, SIZE and TOR to make new words?

b What animal can you put in front of ROD, PART, SHACKLE and PAGE to make new words? *RAM*

c What three letters can surround P, V and X and make new words?

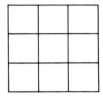

Now track through the grid and find an average of 34 words and a brainbox figure of 56 words.

177 SPECIAL REVERSE TRACKWORD

Here is a full list of 62 words extracted from a Trackword Grid, not including the three nine-letter words that can be correctly tracked.

Can you fill the empty grid in?

ACT ACTED ACTION ACUTE ATE ATOC ATONE ATONED
AUCTION AUTO CAT CATION CAUTION CUD CUE CUED
CUT CUTE CIT CITE CITED COED CON CONE CONED
CONTE COT COTE DEN DENT DEUTON DUCAT DUCT DUE
DUET EDUCT EDUCTION EON ETA ICON ION IOTA ITA
NEO NET NOCTUA NOETIC NOT NOTE NOTED OCA ONE
OTIC TAU TED TEN TIC TOE TOED TON TONE TONED

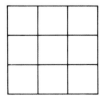

ANSWERS AT A GLANCE

(Those marked * have full explanations or solutions from page 49)
(The full lists of 'TRACKWORD' words start on page 69)

1   *King of Hearts
2   B
3   MAMMALS: cat, rhinoceros, dog, bear, ox, rat, ape, ass, gnu, pig, cow, camel, ewe, sheep, deer, stoat, anteater, boar, shrew, orang, sow, okapi, bat, wolf, dingo
    BIRDS: swan, tit, hen
    FISH: ling
    INSECT: ant
4   *Jerry
5   *1
6   SUPERTED, RUPERT THE BEAR, YOGI, BOOBOO, WINNIE THE POOH, PADDINGTON, BALOO, BIFFO, BARNEY, BIG TED, LITTLE TED, SOOTY
7   *d
8   *Q, X, Y
9   *Shunt, Glory
10 REMAINDER
11 OUTGROWTH
12 KINETICAL
13 3 Goals in a Hat Trick
14 8 Legs of an Octopus
15 1 2 Buckle My Shoe
16 The Prime Minister Lives at 10 Downing Street
17 A 4 Minute Mile
18 8 Furlongs in a Mile
19 6 Pockets on a Snooker Table
20 1 2 3 4 5 Once I Caught a Fish Alive
21 Around the World in 80 Days

22 3 Points for a Win, 1 for a Draw
23 *Scary Mary
    Spooky Luke
    Creepy Crispin
    Eerie Eve
24 Dr (D)ALEK & CYBE(R)MAN
25 *7
26 944
27 *54
28 *3
29 DOCTORATE
30 HAPPINESS
31 MAGNESITE
32 *Sweden
33 *Medway
34 *Thames
35 *Cerebral
36 I understand you intend to underpay my overtime for undertaker's work
37 *Room 16
38 *Radio Times
39 *41
40 *2
41 *Yes
42 ZOOLOGIST
43 NOSTALGIC
44 NUMERICAL
45 Up in arms
46 Somewhere over the rainbow way up high (weigh a pi)
47 Let's face up to it
48 Up against the odds
49 Let off the hook
50 White and black

51 *6
52 *94
53 From left: Olga Oojit, Ivy Igglend, Sue Sploknorst, Annie Armbustrage, Fanny Faskie, Harriet Howzyafather
54 We should see a 3 not a 5 reflected in the mirror. You can see all six faces
55 HEARTLESS
56 EXEMPLARY
57 EASTENDER
58 *Chipmunk
59 YES: Golf, Bind, Hemp, Jack
60 Lip
61 *John Lennon
62 *Sentence
63 *71
64 90
65 2's Company, 3's a Crowd
66 240 Old Pence in a Pound
67 76 Trombones in the Big Parade
68 Snow White and the 7 Dwarfs
69 8 Pints in a Gallon
70 2 Lovely Black Eyes
71 26 Letters of the Alphabet
72 15 Men in a Rugby Union Team
73 20 000 Leagues Under the Sea
74 6 Feet in a Fathom
75 12 Signs of the Zodiac
76 9 Planets of the Solar System
77 6 Characters in Search of an Author
78 12 People on a Jury
79 5 Limbs of a Starfish
80 1 Man Went to Mow
81 We 3 Kings of Orient Are
82 She's Got the Key of the Door Never Been 21 Before
83 The 6 Wives of Henry 8
84 Anne of 1000 Days
85 *31

86 *30
87 *4
88 *Bill & Kate
89 *£11.00
90 *Common section of two interconnecting cylinders at rightangles to each other
91 *Cinderella
92 *Robin Hood
93 *They all end in 'U'
94 CREMASTER
95 DECATHLON
96 SCRAMBLED
97 Where there's a will there's a way
98 Mixed blessings
99 Once upon a time
100 In one ear and out the other
101 Much ado about nothing
102 *6 of Diamonds, 2nd from left (9C, 6D, 8S, 7H)
103 *Butcher
104 *ALPHABETICAL ORDER: Missing double letters
105 Hobby, Noddy, Peewit, Puffin, Swallow, Gannet, Cuckoo, Dipper, Parrot, Bittern
106 *Money
107 They were all girls
108 PROMENADE
109 FORWARDED
110 MASTERFUL
111 Awkward, Dawdler, Cowslip, Dewdrop, Frowsty, News-boy, Growths
112 *Victoria & Albert
113 7
114 *Patricia & Alan
115 *20
116 420
117 c
118 BROCADE: (Bittern, Rabbit, Orbit, Cubit, Ambition, Debit, Exhibit)

119 Grubby, Rugby, Ruby, Buy, By
120 STEAM (stem, mast, meat, east, seam)
121 NEWSPAPER
122 JUSTIFIED
123 HYPOCRITE
124 Keep something under your hat
125 Eternal triangle
126 Cut a long story short
127 The little things in life
128 Many a slip twixt cup and lip
129 *D
130 Don't beat about the bush
131 Lick the habit
132 Hang in the balance
133 Rising damp
134 Underneath the arches
135 *Half a fruitcake
136 *TN'SI
137 QUEUING others are Spontaneous, Ingenuous, Monotonous, Mountainous, Onions, Cannon, Canoeing, Quinine, Inane, Aonian, Pronoun, Trunnion
138 *6
139 Laugh, Giggle, Grin, Titter, Hoot
140 SMIRK (Snigger sMile snIcker choRtle chucKle)
141 *Jacob Puckeridge married Daphne Shotover
Su-Ellen Puckeridge married Algernon Shotover
Archibald Puckeridge married Ermintrude Shotover
142 90 Degrees in a Right Angle
143 1 Referee and 2 Linesmen
144 30 Days in April June September and November
145 6 or 8 Bits in a Byte
146 Cat o' 9 Tails
147 3 Men in a Boat

148 X Equals 10 in Roman Numerals
149 5 Sides of a Pentagon
150 12 Inches in a Foot
151 16 Ounces in a Pound
152 212 Degrees Fahrenheit is the Boiling Point of Water
153 A Four Leaf Clover
154 1984 was Written by George Orwell
155 Fat Fair and 40
156 28 Days in February
157 31 Days in January and July
158 366 Days in a Leap Year
159 24 Hours from Tulsa
160 3 Coins in a Fountain
161 60 Seconds in a Minute
162 *a YELLOW (or WHITE) SQUARE
b 17 YATS = 1 NORG
c £1,332,936
163 *a = Straight line letters
b = Roman numerals 3 straight lines
c = Five-letter words
d = Curved numbers
e = Words end in E
f = Numerals of time
g = Roman numerals use 3 symbols
h = Words begin with T
164 *Pumpkin
165 SPREADING
166 CARTWHEEL
167 PLASTERER
168 *DIS, 25 times
169 I, In, Sin, Sing, Sting, String, Staring, Starling, Startling
170 *SAMPLING
171 *   Joseph (0)
Harry (3)   Gertie (1)
Isobel (4)   Fred (2)
172 *Pup, Poop
173 *DO17O4 WA73O9
174 *1–1

175 *Reverend Green, with the rope in the hall

176 CAP
RAM
OEN = CAMPANERO

177 ION
CTE
AUD = AUCTIONED, CAUTIONED, EDUCA-TION

FULL SOLUTIONS

1 HANDFUL King of Hearts

We must have seen the back of every card, as the same value does not occur in each row. Similarly we must have seen all the faces. This means that one colour back must be repeated as well as one value. As the A-C (Ace of Clubs) only occurs once in the last hand it must have a RED or BLUE back. Similarly the BLACK backed card must be the 2-H (Two of Hearts) or the 5-D (Five of Diamonds). (*Both cards of the wrong colour.*)

However the A-C cannot be the red card because then no card could have the same colour back as its suit.

The A-C must be the blue-backed card.

These four alternatives are developed below:

	HAND 1	BLUE	YELL	RED	KH	5D	2H	*turned over*
	HAND 2	BLUE		3C			2H	[RED GRN 5D]
	HAND 3	AC		3C			BLCK	[YELL GRN KH]
	then 1	BLUE	YELL	RED	**KH**	5D	2H	
	2	BLUE	5D	3C	**RED**	GRN	2H	
	3	AC	YELL	3C	**KH**	GRN	BLCK	
OR	1	BLUE	YELL	RED	KH	5D	2H	*turned over*
	2	BLUE	3C				2H	[RED GRN 5D]
	3	AC	3C				BLCK	[YELL GRN KH]
	then 1	BLUE	YELL	**RED**	KH	5D	2H	
	2	BLUE	3C	**RED**	GRN	5D	2H	
	3	AC	3C	**KH**	GRN	YELL	BLCK	
OR	1	BLUE	YELL	RED	KH	5D	2H	*turned over*
	2	BLUE		3C		5D		[RED GRN 2H]
	3	AC		3C		BLCK		[YELL GRN KH]
	then 1	BLUE	YELL	RED	**KH**	5D	2H	
	2	BLUE	2H	3C	**RED**	5D	GRN	
	3	AC	YELL	3C	**KH**	BLCK	GRN	
OR	1	BLUE	YELL	RED	KH	5D	2H	*turned over*
	2	BLUE	3C			5D		[RED GRN 2H]
	3	AC	3C			BLCK		[YELL GRN KH]
	then 1	BLUE	YELL	**RED**	KH	5D	2H	
	2	BLUE	3C	**RED**	GRN	5D	2H	
	3	AC	3C	**KH**	GRN	BLCK	YELL	

As can be seen, although there are four separate solutions, the only card in each solution that has the same colour back as suit is the K-H, King of Hearts.

4 MONTHS   Jerry

The letter J begins 3 months
  January, June, July

The letter E occurs 11 times in all the months put together
  fEbruary, junE, sEptEmbEr, octobEr, novEmbEr, dEcEmbEr

The letter R occurs in 8 months
  januaRy, febRuaRy, maRch, apRil, septembeR, octobeR, novembeR, decembeR

The letters R & Y end 4 months each
  septembeR, octobeR, novembeR, decembeR
  januarY, februarY, maY, julY

5 CHOCOLATE DROPS   1

Only one weighing is needed.

Number the tubes from 1–20.
Take one chocolate drop from the first tube, then two from the second, three from the third etc, until you take all twenty from the twentieth tube.

You now have 210 chocolate drops.

Weigh them.
Their total weight if they were all the same (5 gms each) should be 1050 gms. But some drops only weigh 4 gms each.

So the weight will be lighter by the number of grams that is the same as the number of the tube.

eg: If the total weight is 1047 gms, it means that 3 of the 210 drops must be lighter. 3 drops came from the third tube.

7 MOVE ROUND   d

The ○ moves to each corner in a clockwise direction.
The × moves to each corner in a counter-clockwise direction.
The + moves to the opposite corner.

8 STRANGE TALE   Q-X-Y

AArdwolf, raBBit, MeCCa, hiDDen, agrEEd, oFF, biGGer, witHHeld, skIIng, haJJ, treKKer, teLL, tuMMies, buNNy, lOOks, sliPPery/triPPed/traPPed/haPPily, (QQ), fuRRy, paSSing, boTTom, cardUUs, boVVer, poWWow, (XX), (YY), whiZZed

9 SWAP FIVE   SHUNT=GLORY

The sentence reads as follows:
'The five substitutes can be deduced within this sentence, which hasn't used them in it.'

23 GHOSTS

WHITE = SCARY MARY
DOTTY = SPOOKY LUKE
SQUAREY = CREEPY CRISPIN
STRIPEY = EERIE EVE

To discover which ghost is which form a grid as follows:

	white	dotty	squarey	stripey
SPOOKY LUKE	·	·	·	·
EERIE EVE	·	·	·	·
SCARY MARY	·	·	·	·
CREEPY CRISPIN	·	·	·	·

We can cross out certain combinations because of the information given:
Stripey is a girl. Scary Mary is not squarey and cannot be dotty or stripey because they are not next to the dotty ghost. Spooky Luke is not next to Eve.

	white	dotty	squarey	stripey
SPOOKY LUKE	·	·	·	×
EERIE EVE	·	·	·	·
SCARY MARY	·	×	×	×
CREEPY CRISPIN	·	·	·	×

	white	dotty	squarey	stripey
SPOOKY LUKE	×	·	·	×
EERIE EVE	×	×	×	·
SCARY MARY	·	×	×	×
CREEPY CRISPIN	×	·	·	×

From this we know that Scary Mary is the white ghost and Eerie Eve is the stripey ghost. If Spooky Luke is not next to Eve he cannot be squarey, and the rest follows:

	white	dotty	squarey	stripey
SPOOKY LUKE	×	·	×	×
EERIE EVE	×	×	×	·
SCARY MARY	·	×	×	×
CREEPY CRISPIN	×	×	·	×

(The Creepy Crispin clue is irrelevant)

25 FOOTBALL POINTS 7

Total matches = 11

If w = number of wins, then $11 - w$ = number of draws.

If all the wins were home wins then

$$\text{league points} = \text{pools points}$$
$$\text{win} + \text{draw} = \text{score draw} + \text{home win}$$
$$(w \times 3) + ((11 - w) \times 2) = ((11 - w) \times 3) + (w \times 1)$$

Therefore
$$3w + 22 - 2w = 33 - 3w + w$$
$$3w = 11$$
$$w = 3.666$$

If all the wins were away wins then

$$\text{league points} = \text{pools points}$$
$$\text{win} + \text{draw} = \text{score draw} + \text{away win}$$
$$(w \times 3) + ((11 - w) \times 2) = ((11 - w) \times 3) + (w \times 1.5)$$

Therefore
$$3w + 22 - 2w = 33 - 3w + 3w/2$$
$$5w = 22$$
$$w = 4.4$$

Neither of these answers is a whole number (one cannot have 3.666 wins). The only whole number between 3.666 and 4.4 is 4, which means there were a combination of home wins and away wins.

If wins = 4 and draws = 7, then

$$\text{league points} = \text{win} + \text{draw}$$
$$= (4 \times 3) + (7 \times 2) = 26$$

Therefore
$$\text{pools points} = \text{score draws} + z$$
$$26 = (7 \times 3) + z$$

where
$$z = \text{number of points from both home and away}$$
$$\text{wins from 4 games.}$$

$$z = 5$$

The only combination possible is 2 home wins = 2, +2 away wins = 3.

27 TENNIS 54

There were 55 pairs, each pair except the winners had to lose once. 54 pairs lost once, there were therefore 54 games.

28 WEIGHINGS 3

Take the twelve bars of chocolate and divide them into three lots of four.

WEIGHING 1
Weigh 4 v 4.
If they balance take the other four and mark these A, B, C & D, also mark one of the other eight Z; then proceed to WEIGHING 2A
If they do not balance mark the ones that go up L′, L″, L‴, L⁗ for light, and the ones that go down H′, H″, H‴, H⁗ for heavy, and the four you haven't weighed mark N for normal, and proceed to WEIGHING 2B

> WEIGHING 2A
> Weigh A&B v C&Z
> If this balances then D is either light or heavy: proceed to WEIGHING 3A
> If the left side goes down then either A or B are heavy, or C is light: proceed to WEIGHING 3B
> If the right side goes down then either A or B are light, or C is heavy: proceed to WEIGHING 3C

>> *WEIGHING 3A*
>> *Weigh D v Z*
>> If the left side goes down *D is heavy*
>> If the right side goes down *D is light*

>> *WEIGHING 3B*
>> *Weigh A v B*
>> If they balance then *C is light*
>> If the left side goes down then *A is heavy*
>> If the right side goes down then *B is heavy*

>> *WEIGHING 3C*
>> *Weigh A v B*
>> If they balance then *C is heavy*
>> If the left side goes down then *B is light*
>> If the right side goes down then *A is light*

> *WEIGHING 2B*
> *Weigh L′+L″+H′ v L‴+H″+N*
> If they balance then either H‴ or H⁗ must be heavy or L⁗ must be light: proceed to WEIGHING 3D
> If the left side goes down then either H′ is heavy or L‴ is light: proceed to WEIGHING 3E
> If the right side goes down then either L′ or L″ are light or H″ is heavy: proceed to WEIGHING 3F

>> *WEIGHING 3D*
>> *Weigh H‴ v H⁗*
>> If they balance then *L⁗ is light*
>> If the left side goes down then *H‴ is heavy*
>> If the right side goes down then *H⁗ is heavy*

53

WEIGHING 3E
Weigh H' v N
If they balance then L''' is light
If the left side goes down then H' is heavy
If the right side goes down then something is very wrong

WEIGHING 3F
Weigh L' v L''
If they balance then H'' is heavy
If the left side goes down then L'' is light
If the right side goes down then L' is light

Quick check of weighings

1A	4 v 4	Balance	2A	AB v CZ	Balance	3A	D v Z
					L Down	3B	A v B
					R Down	3C	A v B
		L or R down	2B	LLH v LHN	Balance	3D	H v H
					L Down	3E	H v N
					R Down	3F	L v L

32 FLAGS Sweden

Sweden's national flag is light blue and yellow; all the others are red, white and blue.

33 BRITISH RIVERS Medway

Avon Mole Ystwyth Derwent Esk Wear

34 MORE RIVERS Thames

Mekong Amazon Severn Hudson Elster Tigris

35 ER Cerebral

Where I read s I see e and where I read e I see r. If I see the word cerebral what should it really be?

37 SCHOOL ROOMS Room 16

If the gym is Room 1, the geography room is Room 14 and the room opposite the chemistry lab is Room 12, the plan of the school building looks like this:

BACK	BOTTOM FLOOR	?	?	?
	MIDDLE FLOOR	?	?	12
	TOP FLOOR	? (music)	?	?

FRONT	TOP FLOOR	? (art)	14 (geog)	?
	MIDDLE FLOOR	?	? (maths)	? (chem)
	BOTTOM FLOOR	?	?	1 (gym)

What logical numbering system fits?

BACK	4	5	6		4	5	6
	10	11	12		9	8	7
	16	17	18		16	17	18

this fits   this does not

FRONT	15	14	13		15	14	13
	9	8	7		10	11	12
	3	2	1		3	2	1

The music room is therefore No 16.

38 FIRST AND LAST Radio Times

ToaD MoosE SkI IgloO ArmchaiR

39 MY FAT FRIEND 41 UMs

My dUMpy chUM hUMphrey Köhler, with an UMlaut, lives in hUMberside with his jUMbo mUM. His house is a bit of a slUM, but he doesn't grUMble – he's never grUMpy or glUM. He's always consUMing nUMerous scrUMptious things, such as satsUMas, kUMquats and pUMpkins, plUM crUMble, rUM dUMplings and UMpteen crUMpets; he's also always chewing lUMpy gUM or hUMbugs. As you can assUMe, his tUMmy is volUMinously plUMp and I think he's a bit of a chUMp. But enough of this bunkUM about the traUMas of hUMphrey's diet. Let's get to the hUMdrUM point of this conundrUM. What is the maximUM nUMber of missing UMs in this hUMble tale?

40 SWEETS 2

To start with I had n sweets.

My friend ate $n/2$. I ate 1. Then my friend ate $\dfrac{n/2-1}{2}$ and I ate 1.

Therefore

$$n = n/2 + 1 + \frac{n/2-1}{2} + 1$$

$$2n = n + 2 + n/2 - 1 + 2$$
$$n/2 = 3$$
$$n = 6$$

41 TENNIS TOURNAMENT   Yes

> Men's Finals = Man1 v Man2
> Ladies Finals = Lady1 v Lady2
> Mixed Finals = Man1 & Lady1 v Man2 & Lady3

Man1, Man2 & Lady1 didn't lose a match before the finals.

51 POURINGS   6

Letter the three containers from left to right A, B & C.

At the beginning:

	A	B	C
	5	3	0 litres

The pourings:

		A	B	C
1	B to C	5	0	3
2	A to B	2	3	3
3	B to C	2	0	6
4	A to B	0	2	6
5	C to A	5	2	1
6	A to B	4	3	1

A has 4 litres in it.

52 TOWERS   94

The ten rings in order of size are:

1Y	(25.4 cm)
2R	(25 cm)
3R	(20.32 cm)
4G	(20 cm)
5G	(15.24 cm)
6Y	(15 cm)
7R	(10.16 cm)
8G	(10 cm)
9Y	(5.08 cm)
10R	(5 cm)

There are 94 combinations of 5 descending order sizes without the same colours appearing next to each other.

53   THE QUEUE   From left:
Olga Oojit
Ivy Igglend
Sue Sploknorst
Annie Armbustrage
Fanny Faskie
Harriet Howzyafather

Setting out the ladies and positions in the queue on a grid we can deduce the following:

	1	2	3	4	5	6
Olga		×	×	×	×	
Ivy			×			
Fanny			×			
Harriet	×	×	×	×		
Sue		×		×		
Annie	×	×			×	×

O wears a red hat

I & F facing same way

H sees 3 hats

S hates blue

Lady on A's right

If Ivy is 2 places ahead of Annie she cannot be in positions 4, 5 or 6.
If Fanny has pushed into the queue she is not in position 6.
Therefore:

	1	2	3	4	5	6
Olga		×	×	×	×	
Ivy			×	×	×	×
Fanny			×			×
Harriet	×	×	×	×		
Sue		×		×		
Annie	×	×			×	×

If Ivy is position 1, then Fanny facing the same way is position 4 and there is nobody to go into position 2 as only I or F can be in position 2.
So Ivy must be in position 2, and the rest follows:

	1	2	3	4	5	6
Olga		×	×	×	×	×
Ivy	×		×	×	×	×
Fanny	×	×	×	×		×
Harriet	×	×	×	×	×	
Sue	×	×		×	×	×
Annie	×	×	×		×	×

58 ANIMALS   Chipmunk

Cow Hare pIg aPe Moose bUll skuNk yaK

61 TABLE   John Lennon

All are anagrams of The Beatles:

> George Harrison
> Ringo Starr
> Paul McCartney

62 OOPS   Sentence

'?Ecnetnes' should not have a capital E

63 SECRET LETTERS   71

This is a picture of a secret gardeN guarded by a Nasty gNome who has stoleN a
letter from it. He woN't let aNybody iN uNless they kNow the letter.
Two childreN called Nora aNd Nick kNow the missiNg letter. 'It is N,' said Nick.
'Now caN we pick some ruNNer beaNs for our diNNer?' 'No!' griNNed the gNome,
scratchiNg his loNg Nose. 'IN here you caN oNly pick Nasturtiums, aNemoNes aNd
peoNies.' 'ANd Noses, by the look of you,' Nora sNiggered. 'That's uNfair,' Nick
sNarled. 'We waNt ruNNer beaNs with our joiNt.' 'Oh! all right theN,' the gNome
sNiffed, aNd wiNked wickedly. 'If you caN couNt up the exact Number of missiNg
Ns iN this story, you caN pick whatever you waNt.' 'ThaNk you,' they said, aNd
they did. So they got their ruNNer beaNs for their diNNer.

85 ALPHABETICAL NAMES   31

Abel, Amos, Amy, Ann, Bee, Ben, Bert, Berty, Bess, Bessy, Betty, Bill, Billy, Bo,
Cissy, Cy, Di, Dot, Ed, Emmy, Fitz, Flo, Guy, Ivy, Jo, Jos, Joy, Lot, Lotty, Ray, Su.

86 LACITEBAHPLA SEMAN   30

Ed, Eda, Ida, La, Lea, Lee, Lu, Ned, Olga, Oona, Poll, Rea, Rod, Rolf, Rolfe, Roma,
Ron, Rona, Seb, Sid, Sonia, Ted, Tom, Ulla, Una, Vi, Vic, Yvonne, Zia, Zoe.

87 RELATIONS   4

Chris is a girl.

88 MORE RELATIONS   Bill & Kate

From the information we can see who is married to whom:
John m. Mary   Nick m. Rita   Bill m. Kate

Let the average age = n

Mary (n) is Bill's (n−1) elder sister
Nick (n+1) is Mary's elder brother
Kate (n) is Rita's (n−1) elder sister
Kate's elder brother is Bill's brother-in-law, who must be John (n+1)

Therefore:

John A (n+1) m. Mary B (n)   TOTAL = 2n+1
Nick B (n+1) m. Rita A (n−1)   = 2n
Bill B   (n−1) m. Kate A (n)   = 2n−1

The combined ages of Bill & Kate are the least.

89 TILES   £11.00

The problem here is not whether it is possible to get a different looking tile in each vertical, horizontal or diagonal from the 14 available shapes, which it is, but what is the cheapest way of buying them.
The 14 different shapes are Tile A, B (4 ways up), C (2 ways), D, E (2 ways) and F (4 ways).

Getting   24 B @ £4
and   24 F @ £4
plus   8 A @ £1.50
plus   8 C @ £1.50

Total   £11.00

Gives enough shapes and is the cheapest.

90 OBJECTIVE   Common section of two interconnecting cylinders at right angles to each other

The two tubes below intersect at right angles. The volume which is common to both tubes gives a shape which is circular from A, circular from B and square from the top.

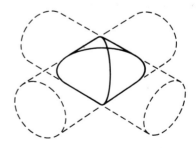

91 CHRISTMAS THINGS Cinderella

deCorations
reIndeer
saNta
puDding
trEe
caRd
quEen
beLl
hoLly
crAcker

92 PANTOMIMES Robin Hood

a CindeRella
b Toad of TOad Hall
c BaBes in the Wood
d Dick WhittIngton
e RobinsoN Crusoe
f Humpty Dumpty
g MOther Goose
h Puss in BoOts
i Jack anD the Beanstalk

93 OVER TO YOU They all end in 'U'

a Frau
b Zebu
c Hindu or Urdu
d Adieu
e Flu
f Emu
g Menu
h Gnu
i You
j Impromptu

102   FOUR CARDS   6 of Diamonds 2nd from left
(9C, 6D, 8S, 7H)

The club is to the left of the heart.

6 Alternatives:

C	H	–	–
C	–	H	–
C	–	–	H
–	C	H	–
–	C	–	H
–	–	C	H

But for the 7H to be 2 away from a card between two others must mean it is on the end.

so:

C	–	–	7H
–	C	–	7H
–	–	C	7H

8S is next to the card immediately to the right of the club:

C	–	8S	7H

The two highest cards in the sequence must be 8 and 9.

Therefore

9C	–	8S	7H

and the second card must be the 6D.

103   TRADESMEN   Butcher

The question is to find out what trade Mr Baker has, you do not need to find out what the others do or where they live. In fact there is not enough information for you to do the latter anyway. In all six alternative combinations Mr Baker is always the butcher as follows. Mr Smith cannot live in the middle house. As Mr Turner and Mr Grocer live three doors from each other neither can live in the middle house. The butcher lives in the middle house and no tradesman bears the name of his trade so it cannot be Mr Butcher. So the butcher can only be Mr Baker.

104   ANIMALS   Alphabetical: missing double letters

giBBon, chEEtah, giraFFe, LLama, leMMing, babOOn, feRRet, opoSSum, poTTo

106   MASTERWORD   Money

O in COAST, E in TIRED, Y in YACHT, M in MIRTH, N in STAND

112   DUOS   Victoria & Albert

Victoria & Albert are the only male/female duo.
The others are: Laurel & Hardy, Abbott & Costello, Little & Large, Gladstone & Disraeli, Morecambe & Wise, Cannon & Ball and Flanagan & Allen.

114   NAMES   Patricia & Alan

Alan only starts with the last letter of PatriciA, all the others start with the last two letters of the previous name: AlAN NAoMI MIKE KEiTH THelMA MArtIN INgrID IDA DAvid

115   LINES   20

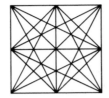

129   LETTERED CARDS   D

The only two ways that 3 cards can be in different positions each time is as follows: (assigning numbers for each card)

$$
\begin{array}{ccc} 1 & 2 & 3 \\ 2 & 3 & 1 \\ 3 & 1 & 2 \end{array}
\quad \text{or} \quad
\begin{array}{ccc} 1 & 2 & 3 \\ 3 & 1 & 2 \\ 2 & 3 & 1 \end{array}
$$

If we look at the first arrangement card 3 has the letters C, D & B on it, which is impossible, so the second arrangement must be correct.

$$
\begin{array}{lll}
1 = A & 2 = B & 3 = C \\
3 = C & 1 = D & 2 = C \quad \text{Cards 1 \& 2 turned over} \\
2 = B & 3 = A & 1 = ? \quad \text{Cards 2 \& 3 turned over}
\end{array}
$$

Therefore card 1 should show a D.

135   FRUITCAKE   Half a fruitcake

The equation is as follows:

$$18 + \tfrac{1}{2} + 6 - \tfrac{1}{2} - 15 = 9 = \text{Half a fruitcake}$$

136   KCAB   TN'SI

Should read T'NSI = ISN'T backwards

138   OOE TO FIVE   6

$$
\begin{array}{l}
1+2+3-4-5 = -1-2 \\
1+2-3+4-5 = 1-2 \\
1+2-3-4+5 = -1+2 \\
1-2+3+4-5 = -1+2 \\
1-2+3-4+5 = 1+2 \\
1-2-3-4+5 = -1-2
\end{array}
$$

141 SIBLINGS Jacob m. Daphne
Su-Ellen m. Algernon
Archibald m. Ermintrude

If there are to be more Puckeridges than Shotovers after marriage then there must be either 3 Puckeridge men or 2 Puckeridge men and 1 Puckeridge lady. As Su-Ellen has no sisters she cannot be a Shotover and must be a Puckeridge.
We therefore have:

Mr ? Puckeridge m. Miss ? Shotover
Mr ? Puckeridge m. Miss ? Shotover
Mr ? Shotover m. Miss Su-Ellen Puckeridge

Jacob is Ermintrude's sister's husband:

Mr Jacob Puckeridge m. Miss ? Shotover
Mr ? Puckeridge m. Miss Ermintrude Shotover
Mr ? Shotover m. Miss Su-Ellen Puckeridge

Algernon is married to the sister of Daphne's husband

Mr Jacob Puckeridge m. Miss Daphne Shotover
Mr ? Puckeridge m. Miss Ermintrude Shotover
Mr Algernon Shotover m. Miss Su-Ellen Puckeridge

The other Puckeridge is Archibald

162 BOTOBIAN MONEY a Yellow (or white) square
b 17 yats = 1 norg
c £1,332,936

a

11 gimlips = 1 nogwod
3 nogwods = 1 yat, i.e.: 33 gimlips = 1 yat
Exchange rate 17 gimlips = £1

The values of the coins shown are:

Blue triangle (3 edges)	=	3 nogwods	=	33 gimlips
Red square (4 edges)	=	4 yat	=	132 gimlips
White circle (1 edge)	=	1 gimlip	=	1 gimlip
Green cross (12 edges)	=	12 nogwods	=	132 gimlips
Yellow star (10 edges)	=	10 gimlips	=	10 gimlips
Pink hexagon (6 edges)	=	6 yat	=	198 gimlips

Total = 506 gimlips
£30 = 30×17 = 510 gimlips   Therefore   510−506 = 4.

4 gimlips are needed which could be a white or yellow square

b The first number of gimlips which would be exactly divisible by yats and by 17 is
33×17 = 561.
561 gimlips = **1 norg** = **17 yats** or £33
c   561 norgs = 1 zmukki = £33×561 = £18,513
6×12 sided zmukkis = £18,513×6×12 = **£1,332,936**

163 GROUPS a = straight line letters
b = roman numerals 3 straight lines
c = 5-letter words
d = curved numbers
e = words end in e
f = numerals of time
g = roman numerals use 3 symbols
h = words begin with t

a = FIVE NINE TEN ELEVEN FIFTEEN etc

b = III IV VI IX XI LI etc.

c = Three Seven Eight Forty Fifty Sixty

d = 2 3 5 6 8 9 10 etc.

e = onE threE fivE ninE twelvE twenty-onE etc.

f = 4 seasons = one year, 7 days = one week, 10 years = one decade,
12 months = one year, 24 hours = one day, 60 seconds = one minute,
60 minutes = one hour, 100 years = one century, 1000 years = one millennium

g = III, VII, XII, XVI, XIX, XXI, XXV, XXX, XLI, XLV, LII etc.

h = Two, Three, Ten, Twelve, Thirteen, Twenty-one etc.

164 MENU Pumpkin

The menu should have read:

Pea soUp

*   *   *

gaMe Pie
with
Kale & chIps

*   *   *

flaN

168 A AGREEABLE DAY 25 DISs

A DISagreeable day

The same three letters have been DIScarded from the beginning of a number of words in this puzzle. Can you DIScover them and how many times they are missing?

'It was a DISmal day and I could DIScern DISaster in the air as I washed up the DISgustingly dirty breakfast DISHes and DIScussed with my DIStinctly DIStressed mother the DISturbances we had recently had in the DIStrict. The day before a group of demonstrators showed a lack of DIScipline while being DISpersed by the police and had trampled across our garden. The DIStinguished DISc jockey who lives next door was DISputing our rights of way. Our DIShevelled dog had got DIStemper. Dad had lost his job at the DIStillery, and a DIStant aunt was coming to stay. I DISpelled by DIStraught mother's worst fears and decided to DIStance myself for a day or two.'

170 ELEMENTARY Sampling

Sodium (NA), Antimony (SB), Mercury (HG), Potassium (K), Lead (PB), Iron (FE), Nitrogen (N), Gold (AU)

171 BIRTHDAY CARDS

Cards given by each friend 4, 3, 2, 1 & 0.
Cards received by each friend 2.

JOSEPH (0)

HARRY (3)   GERTIE (1)

ISOBEL (4)   FRED (2)

	Gave	Received	From
Fred	2	2	
Gertie	1	2	
Harry	?	2	G &
Isobel	?	2	
Joseph	0	2	

Joseph sits next to Harry. Isobel cannot be next to Joseph.

As G has given her one card to H, I cannot sit next to G.

Similarly F cannot have G on his left

Therefore

	Gave	Received	From
Fred	2	2	H & I
Gertie	1	2	F & I
Harry	3	2	G & I
Isobel	4	2	F & H
Joseph	0	2	H & I

172 WORD GAMES Pup Poop

ANNA is to BOB (1 letter on, middle double letter to single)
OTTO+1 = PUUP drop double = PUP

DAD is to DEED (Next vowel up made double)
PIP = POOP

173 CODE DO17O4 WA73O9

Assume the last sentence starts with an interrogative

$$W8A7 = \text{WHAT} \quad 8 = H \quad 7 = T$$

Then the first word 780 = THE, so 0 = E and the paragraph looks like this:

THE 15E6E4 DETE1TI6E I96E9TED BY 3I4 A4THU4 1O9A9 DOY5E I3, OF 1OU43E, 3HE45O12 HO5ME3. WHAT I3 HI3 A33I3TA9T'S 9AME, I9 1ODE?

The last sentence must start 'What iS hiS . . .' and it is pretty clear that the number 1 stands for 'C'

$$3 = S \qquad 1 = C$$

THE C5E6E4 DETECTI6E I96E9TED BY SI4 A4THU4 CO9A9 DOY5E IS, OF COU4SE, SHE45OC2 HO5MES. WHAT IS HIS ASSISTA9T'S 9AME, I9 CODE?

'Of couRse' is pretty clear of course, and the rest should follow:

$$4 = R \qquad 5 = L \qquad 6 = V \qquad 9 = N \qquad 2 = K$$

THE CLEVER DETECTIVE INVENTED BY SIR ARTHUR CONAN DOYLE IS, OF COURSE, SHERLOCK HOLMES. WHAT IS HIS ASSISTANT'S NAME, IN CODE?

The answer DOCTOR WATSON in code is DO17O4 WA73O9

174 FOOTBALL 1-1

Certain mathematical facts arise as follows:

Each team played 4 games - Max pts available per team = 8

10 games were played in all - Total pts available between 5 teams = 20

All the numbers from 1–9 occur in the goals for and against columns. Therefore we can work out the total goals scored for and against which must be double the total goals scored in the ten matches.

Therefore $\qquad a+b+c+d+e+f+g+h+i = 45$

TOTAL $\qquad$ Goals for and against = 45 + aa

aa cannot = 22 as the TOTAL would be an odd number

If aa = 33 there would be more goals for than against, so aa must = 11
The TOTAL goals for & against = 56
TOTAL goals scored = 28
a = 1 (Of course this could have been gleaned from the fact that Minty's goalie only conceded one goal)

Team	Goals for	Goals against	Points
Minty	11	1	b
Nontown	b	c	d
Oghead	d	e	e
Pester	f	g	h
Queenford	h	i	1

THE NINE LOWEST SCORING GAMES (all the games had different scorelines) ADD UP TO 23 GOALS:

0–0, 1–1, 2–2, 1–0, 2–0, 3–0, 4–0, 2–1, 3–1

Out of the next lowest scoring games 5–0, 4–1 or 3–2 we know that Minty beat Pester 5–0. So the ten score lines are the nine above and 5–0 = 28 goals. A New Table including results given and the fact that Queenford only scored 3 goals therefore h = 3.

Team	Played	M	N	O	P	Q	GF	GA	Pts
Minty		×			5–0		11	1	b
Nontown			×	2–2	3–0		b	c	d
Oghead			2–2	×			d	e	e
Pester		0–5	0–3		×		f	g	3
Queenford						×	3	i	1

As there are only 20 pts to distribute between the five teams the only combination where all their points scores are different is: 1 3 4 5 7 = 20 which must be the points each received. Therefore e = 4, d = 5 and b = 7.

Team	M	N	O	P	Q	GF	GA	Pts			
M	×			5–0		11	1	7	3 wins	1 draw	0 losses
N		×	2–2	3–0		7	c	5	2 wins	1 draw	1 loss
O		2–2	×			5	4	4	1 win	2 draws	1 loss
P	0–5	0–3		×		f	g	3	1 win	1 draw	2 losses
Q					×	3	i	1	0 win	1 draw	3 losses

scores not accounted for: 0–0, 1–1, 1–0, 2–0, 4–0, 2–1, 3–1

More extracted facts: Minty scored in every game so their draw must be 1–1, their other 2 games must be 4–0 & 1–0 to add up to 11–1.

Oghead's Tusker hat-trick could only have been scored in a 3–1 win, their other 2 games must be 0–0 & 0–1 (v Minty) to add up to 5–4.

	M	N	O	P	Q	GF-GA	Pts	Plus
M	×		1-0	5-0		11-1	7	4-0 & 1-1
N		×	2-2	3-0		7-c	5	1 win 1 loss
O	0-1	2-2	×			5-4	4	3-1 & 0-0
P	0-5	0-3		×		f-g	3	1 win 1 draw
Q					×	3-i	1	1 draw 3 losses

As Queenford did not register a win, Nontown must have beaten them, so Nontown lost to Minty. Only draw left (0-0) must be between Oghead and Pester.

	M	N	O	P	Q	GF-GA	Pts	Plus
M	×	4-0	1-0	5-0	1-1	11-1	7	
N	0-4	×	2-2	3-0		7-c	5	1 win
O	0-1	2-2	×	0-0		5-4	4	3-1
P	0-5	0-3	0-0	×		f-g	3	1 win
Q	1-1				×	3-i	1	3 losses

Unused scores: 2-0 & 2-1

	M	N	O	P	Q	GF-GA	Pts	Plus
M	×	4-0	1-0	5-0	1-1	11-1	7	
N	0-4	×	2-2	3-0	2-	7-c	5	1 win
O	0-1	2-2	×	0-0	3-1	5-4	4	
P	0-5	0-3	0-0	×	2-	f-g	3	1 win
Q	1-1	-2	1-3	-2	×	3-i	1	3 losses

f = 2, c cannot = 7, so c must = 6, therefore Nontown beat Queenford 2-0, and Pester beat Queenford 2-1.
g = 9, i = 8

FINAL TABLE

	M	N	O	P	Q	GF-GA	Pts
M	×	4-0	1-0	5-0	1-1	11-1	7
N	0-4	×	2-2	3-0	2-0	7-6	5
O	0-1	2-2	×	0-0	3-1	5-4	4
P	0-5	0-3	0-0	×	2-1	2-9	3
Q	1-1	0-2	1-3	1-2	×	3-8	1

175 A CLUE DOIG Reverend Green, with the Rope in the Hall

'When will this weatheR EVER END, GREENhouses are not the place to be with the dooR OPEn, I sHALL go elsewhere.'

TRACKWORDS FULL WORD LIST

10

Average 43   Brainbox 79

AID AIN AIR AND ARE DAM DAN DEE DIE DIN EAN EAR ERA IDE IND IRE MAD MAE MAN MAR NAE NAM NID RAD RAM RAN RED REE REM RIA RID RIN

ARID DAME DARE DARI DEAN DEAR DEEM DEER DEME DIAN DIRE DRAM DREE EARD EDAM IDEA MADE MAID MAIN MARE MEAD MEAN MEED MEIN MERI NAIR NAME NARD NARE NIDE RADE RAID RAIN RAND RANI RARE READ REAM REAN REAR REED REIN RIDE RIEM RIND

ADEEM AIDER AMEER DINAR DRAIN DREAM DREAR EARED EIDER INDRA IRADE MARID MEDIA NADIR NAMED NAMER RAMEE REDAN REDIA RIDER

DEMAIN DEMEAN MANDIR MEANIE MEDIAN

RAIDER RANDEM RANDIE READER REAMER REDIAE REMADE REMAIN REMAND REMEAD REMEID

AMERIND DREAMER MEANDER READIER REMANIE

REMAINDER

TOTAL 119

11

Average 26   Brainbox 41

GOO GOT HOG HOO HOT HOW OHO ORT OUT ROT ROW THO TOG TOO TOR TOT TOW TWO WOG WOO WOT

GOTH GOUT GROT GROW HOOT HOUT ROOT ROUT ROWT THOR THOU TOHO TOOT TORT TOUT TOWT TROT TROW WOOT WORT

GROUT ORTHO OUTGO ROWTH TOOTH TROTH WORTH WROTH

GROWTH

OUTGROW

OUTGROWTH

TOTAL 52

12

Average 30   Brainbox 51

AIN AIT ALE ANE ATE CAN CAT CIT EAN EAT EIK ETA INK ITA KAE KAI KAT KIN KIT LAC LAT LEA LEI LEN LET NAE NET TAE TAI TAK TAN TEA TEL TEN TIC TIE

AKIN CAIN CANE CATE CITE ELAN KAIN KALE KINA KINE KITE LACK LAIC LAIN LANE LANK LATE LEAK LEAN LEAT NAIK NEAL NEAT TACK TAEL TALE TANE TANK TEAK TEAL TEAN TELA TICK

CITAL ENIAC INLET LATEN LAKIN TAKIN TEIAN TENIA TICAL

KINETIC

KINETICAL

TOTAL 80

29

Average 32   Brainbox 55

ADO ART ATE COD COO COR COT DOE DOO DOR DOT EAR EAT ETA OAR OAT ORD RAD RAT ROC ROD ROE ROT TAE TAR TEA TOD TOE TOO TOR TOT

ATOC COAT CODA CORD COTE COOT DART DATE DOAT DOOR DORA DORT DOTE DRAT EARD RATE ROAD ROOD ROOT ROTA ROTE TARO TART TEAD TEAR TEAT TOAD TOOT TORT TOTE TRAD TROD TROT

OCTET ORATE ROATE TAROT TROAT

DOCTOR

DOCTORATE

TOTAL 71

30

Average 22   Brainbox 38

AIN ANE ASH ASP ASS EAN ESS HAE HAN HAP HAS HEN NAE NAP NAS NIP PAH PAN PAP PIA PIE PIN PIP SAE SAI SAN SAP SEA SEN SHE SPA

APSE HAIN HASP HEAP HESP NEAP NESH NESS NIPA PAIN PANE PASH PASS PINA PINE SAIN SANE SASH SEAN SHAN SHEA SPAE SPAN SPIN

ASHEN SHAPS SPAIN SPANE SPINA SPINE

NAPPIES

HAPPINESS

TOTAL 63

31

Average 37   Brainbox 66

AIM AIN AIT ANE EAN ENS GAE GAM GAN GIE GIN ITS MAE MAG MAN MES MET MIS NAE NAG NAM NIM NIS NIT SEA SEN SET SIN SIT TEA TIE TIG TIN

AGIN EINE EMIT ESNE GAIN GAIT GAME GIEN GEST GITE ITEM MAGI MAIN MANE MEAN MEIN MESE MIEN MINA MINE MING MISE MIST MITE NAME NEST SEAM SEAN SEMI SIEN SIGN SIMA SINE SING SITE SNAG SNIG STEM STIE TEAM TEAN TIME TINE TING

AGIST AMINE ANIME ANISE EIGNE GAMIN INSET MAINS MAISE MANES MANIS MANSE MEANE MEANS MESNE METIS NEIST SEINE SEMIE STEAM STEAN STEIN STIME STING TEIAN

AGNISE ENSEAM GAMINE MAGNES MEANIE MESIAN STEANE

TEAMING

STEAMING

MAGNESITE

TOTAL 112

42

Average 12   Brainbox 20

ITS LIG LIS LIT LOG LOO LOT OIL SIT TIG TIL TOO ZOO

GIST GLIT GLOT LIST LOOT OLIO SILO TOIL TOOL

IGLOO STOOL ZOIST

OOLOGIST

ZOOLOGIST

TOTAL 27

43

Average 46   Brainbox 82

AGO CIG CIT COG COL CON COS COT GAL GAS GAT GIN GIO GOA GOT ION LAG LAT LOG LOS LOT NIT NOG NOT OAT SAG SAL SAT SOC SOG SOL SON SOT TAG TIC TIG TIN TOG TON

AGIN AGIO AGON ASTI ATOC CITS COAL COAT COIN COLA COST GAOL GAST GOAL GOAT ICON IOTA LAST LOCI LOIN LONG LOST LOTA OAST OATS OTIC SAGO SATI SOLA SONG STAG STOA TING TOGA TOLA TONG

ALGIN ALONG CITAL COAST COATI COIGN CONGA COSTA GLOAT INGOT LATIN LOGIC LONGA NOTAL OCTAL SALON SATIN SONIC STING STOIC STOLA TALON TIGON TOING TONGA TONIC

AGONIC ATONIC COSTAL SAGOIN STINGO

COATING COSTING COTINGA GNOSTIC LASTING

AGNOSTIC COASTING

NOSTALGIC

TOTAL 114

44

Average 28   Brainbox 48

AIL AIM AIR ARC ARE ARM CAM CAN CAR EAN EAR EAU ERA IRE LAC LAM LAR LIN MAC MAE MAN MAR MUN NAE NAM NIL RAM RAN REM RIA RIN

ACRE ANIL ARIL CAIN CAME CARE CAUM CIRE CRAM CRAN ERIC LAER LAIC LAIN LAIR LAME LARE LIAR LIRA LIRE MAIL MAIN MALI MARC MARE MAUN MEAL MEAN MERI NAIL NAIR NAME NARE RAIL RAIN RANI RAUN REAL REAM REAN RIAL

CRAME CREAM LINAC MALIC MANIC MERIL NACRE NAMER

NUMERIC

NUMERICAL

TOTAL 82

55

Average 526   Brainbox 85

ALE ALT ARE ART ASH ASS ATE EAR EAT ELT ERA ESS ETA HAE HAS HAT HER HET
LAH LAR LAT LEA LET RAH RAS RAT REH RET SAE SAL SAR SAT SEA SEL SET SHE
TAE TAR TEA TEL

ARET EASE ESSE HAET HALE HALT HARE HART HATE HEAL HEAR HEAT LAER LARE
LASE LASH LASS LATE LEAR LEAT LESS RALE RASE RASH RATE REAL SALE SALT
SATE SEAL SEAR SEAT SESE SETA SHEA TAEL TALE TARE TASH TASS TEAL TEAR
TELA

ALTER ARETE ARTEL ASHET ASSET EASEL EASER EATER ELATE ERASE HALES HATER
HEART LARES LASER LATER LEARE LEASE LEASH RASSE RATEL REATE RESET SELAH
SETAE SHALE SHALT SHARE SHEAL SHEAR TALES TASSE TEASE TELAE TERAS TRASH
TRESS

EASSEL ELATER HALTER LASHER LEASER LESSER RESALE RESEAL RESEAT SAETER
SALTER SEATER TASSEL TEASEL TEASER

ARTLESS HATLESS TESSERA

HEARTLESS

TOTAL 139

56

Average 38   Brainbox 64

ALP AMP APE ARE ARY AXE AYE EAR ERA LAE LAM LAP LAR LAX LAY MAE MAP MAR
MAX MAY PAL PAM PAR PAX PAY PEA PEE PRE RAM RAP RAX RAY REE REX YAM YAP
YEA YEX

AERY EARL EXAM EERY LAER LAME LAMP LARE MARE MARL MEAL PARE PEAL PEAR
PEER PLAY PRAM PRAY PREE PREY RAMP RAPE REAL REAM REAP YARE YEAR

AMEER AMPEX APERY LAYER PAYEE PAYER PEARL PEERY RAMEE

PLAYER

EXEMPLARY

TOTAL 76

57

Average 58   Brainbox 103

AND ANE ARE ART ATE DAN DEE DEN EAN EAR EAT END ERA ETA NAE NAS NET RAD
RAN RAS RAT RED REE RET SAD SAN SAR SAT SEA SEN SET TAE TAN TAR TEA TED
TEE TEN

ARED ARET DANE DARE DART DATE DEAN DEAR DEER EASE EAST ETEN NARE NASE
NEAR NEAT NEST NETE RADE RAND RASE RATE RATS READ REAN REDE REED RETE
SAND SANE SATE SEAN SEAR SEAT SEND SETA STAR STEN TANE TARE TEAD TEAN
TEAR TEED TEND TRAD TREE

AREDE ARETE ASTER DATER DETER EARED EASED EATEN EATER ENATE ENDER
ERASE ESTER NATES RASED RATED REAST REATE REDAN SATED SEDAN SETAE STAND
STADE STANE STARE STEAD STEAN STEED STRAD STRAE TEADE TEASE TERAS TRADE
TREAD TREED

DERATE EASTER ENDART ENDEAR ERASED NEATER NESTED NEARED NESTER REDATE
REEDEN SAETER SANDER SEATED SEDATE SENATE SENDER STARED STEANE STEARE
STRAND TENDER

EASTENDER

TOTAL 145

93

Average 70   Brainbox 120

ACE ARE ARC ARM ART ATE CAM CAR CAT EAR EAT ERA ERE ETA MAC MAE MAR
MAS MAT MES MET RAM RAS RAT REM RET SAC SAE SAM SAR SAT SEA SET TAE TAM
TAR TEA

ACER ACRE ARET CAME CARE CART CASE CAST CATE CEAS CERE CERT CRAM EASE
EAST MACE MARC MARE MART MAST MATE MEAT MERE MESA METE RACE RARE
RASE RATE RATS REAM REAR REST RETE SAME SATE SEAM SEAR SEAT SERE SETA
STAR STEM TACE TAME TARE TEAM TEAR TERM TRAM TSAR

ARETE ARMET ASTER CARER CASTE CATER CATES CEASE CERES CRAME CRARE
CRATE CREAM CREST EATER ERASE ESTER MACER MASER MATER MEASE METER
METRE RACER RATER REARM REAST REATE SATEM SERAC SETAE STARE STEAM
STERE STRAE TAMER TEASE TERAS TERCE TRACE

AMERCE CARTER CASTER CERATE CERMET CERTES CRATER CREASE CREATE EASTER
ECARTE ERASER MASTER MERCAT MERCER RAREST RASTER REAMER RECAST RESTER
SAETER SEARCE SEATER STARER STEARE STREAM TEAMER TEARER TEASER TERMES
TRACER

CATERER CERAMET CREMATE STEAMER

STREAMER

CREMASTER

TOTAL 165

94

Average 40   Brainbox 72

ACE ALT AND ANE CAD CAN CAT CHA CHE DAH DAL DAN DEN EAN EAT END HAD
HAE HAN HAT HEN LAC LAD LAH LAT NAE OAT ONE TAE TAN THE

ACHE CADE CANE CHAD CHAL CHAT DACE DALT DANE DEAL DEAN EACH EATH
HADE HALO HALT HAND HEAD HEAL HEAT HEND HENT LACE LADE LAND LANE
LANT LATH LOAD LOAN LONE NEAL NEAT OATH TACE TACH TANE THAE THAN
THEA THEN

ALONE CANED CANEH CHEAT DEALT DEATH DECAL LACED LADEN LANDE LATHE
LOACH LOATH NACHE NEATH TACHE TALON THANE THECA

LATHED LATHEN LOADEN LOANED LOATHE OATHED THECAL

LOATHED

DECATHLON

TOTAL 100

75

95

Average 66   Brainbox 115

ACE ALB ALE ARC ARE BAD BAM BAR CAB CAD CAM CAR DAB DAL DAM EAR ELD
ELM ERA LAB LAC LAD LAM LAR LEA LED MAB MAC MAD MAE MAR MAS RAD RAM
RAS RED SAB SAC SAD SAE SAL SAM SAR

ABLE ACED ACER ACRE ARED BADE BAEL BALD BALE BALM BARE BLAE BLAM BLED
CADE CALM CARE CRAB CRAM DACE DALE DARE DEAL DEAR EDAM LACE LADE LAER
LAMB LAMS LARE LEAD LEAM LEAR MACE MADE MALE MARC MARE RACE RADE
RALE READ REAL REAM SALE SCAB SCAD SCAR

ABLED ABLER ACRED ALDER AMBLE ARCED BALED BALER BARED BLADE BLARE
BLEAR CABLE CARED CEDAR CREAM DACRE DECAL LACED MACER RACED REALM
SABLE SCALD SCALE SCARE SCRAM

AMBLED AMBLER BALDER CABLED CRADLE CREDAL MARCEL RAMBLE SACRED
SCALED SCALER SCARED SCREAM

RAMBLED SCALDER SCAMBLE

SCAMBLER SCRAMBLE

SCRAMBLED

TOTAL 138

108

Average 45   Brainbox 85

AND ANE ARE DAM DAN DAP DEN EAN EAR END ERA MAD MAE MAN MAP MAR MEN
MOA MOE MOP MOR NAE NAM NAP NED NEO OAR ORD ORE PAD PAM PAN PAR POA
POM PRO RAD RAM RAN RAP RED ROE ROM

AMEN ARED DAME DANE DARE DEAN DEAR DEMO DRAM DRAP DROP EARD EDAM
EDEN MADE MANE MARE MEAD MEAN MEDE MEND MOAN MORA MORE NAME NARD
NARE NEAP NEAR OMEN PANE PAND PARD PARE POEM POME PORE PRAM PROA PROM
RADE RAND READ REAM REAN REAP REDE ROAD ROAM ROAN ROME

AMEND AREDE DREAM DROME EARED EDEMA MANED NAMED NAMER OARED OREAD
PADRE PANED PROEM REDAN ROMAN

ENDEAR MENDER NEARED PANDER POMADE RANDEM

MEANDER

PROMENADE

TOTAL 118

76

109

Average 34   Brainbox 56

ADD ADO ARE DAW DOD DOE DOR DOW ERA ERF FED FOE FOR FRO OAR ODD ODE ORD ORE RAD RAW RED ROD ROE ROW WAD WAR WOE

ARED AROW DARE DOER DORA DRAW DROW EDDA FEOD FORD FORE FROW ORED ORFE OWRE RADE RARE REDD REDO ROAD ROAR RODE ROED WADD WADE WARD WARE WOAD WORD WORE

ADDER ADORE AREDD DARED DORAD DOWAR OARED ODDER ORDER WADED WADER

DEODAR FEDORA FODDER FORDED REDOWA REDRAW ROARED WARDED WARDER WOADED WORDED

FORWARD

FORWARDED

TOTAL 82

110

Average 54   Brainbox 88

ARE ATE AUF EAR EAT EAU ERA ERF ETA FAR FAT FUM LAM LAR LAT LUM MAE MAR MAS MAT RAF RAM RAS RAT REF RET SAE SAL SAM SAR SAT SEA SET SUM TAE TAM TAR TAU TEA TEF USE

ALUM ARET EAST FARE FAST FATE FEAL FEAR FEAT FEST FRAE FRAU FRET FUSE FUST LAER LARE LAST LASE LATE LUST MARE MAST MASU MATE MAUL MUSA MUSE MUST RASE RATE RATS REAL REAM REST SAFE SATE SAUL SEAL SEAM SEAR SEAT SERF SETA SLAE SLAM SLAT SLUM STAR TARE TEAL TEAM TEAR TSAR USER

AMUSE ASTER FALSE FEAST FERAL FETAL LARES LASER LATER MASER MATER MUSER MUSET REAST SAFER SLATE STARE STEAL STEAM TALUS TERAS TESLA

AMUSER AUSTER FALSER FASTER FESTAL LASTER LUSTER MASTER MAUSER MUSTER SLATER

TEARFUL

MASTERFUL

TOTAL 131

121

Average 41   Brainbox 71

APE ARE ASP EAR ENE ERA ERE EWE NEE NEP NEW PAP PAR PEA PEE PEN PEP PER
PEW RAP REE REP SAE SAP SAR SEA SEE SEN SEW SPA WEE WEN

APSE EARN EASE ENEW ERNE EWER NEAP NEAR NEEP NEWS PAPE PARE PEAR PEEN
PEER PREP RAPE RASE RASP REAP REEN REPS SEAR SEEN SEEP SEER SERE SPAE SPAR
SPEW SWEE WEAR WEEN WEEP WERE

ASPEN EASER ERASE NEWER PAPER PEASE PENES PRASE PREEN RENEW SAREE SEWEN
SEWER SPAER SPARE SPEAR SPEER SWEAR SWEEP SWEER

PARPEN SERAPE SPEWER

NEWSPAPER

TOTAL 91

122

Average 16   Brainbox 24

DUE FIE FIT FUD ITS JET JUD JUT SIT SUD SUE SUI TED TUI

DUET DUST ETUI FIST FUST JUST JUTE SITE STUD SUED SUET SUIT UTIS

SITED SUITE

FISTED

JUSTIFIED

TOTAL 31

123

Average 26   Brainbox 42

COP COR COT COY HOE HOP HOT HOY HYP OCH ORC ORT OYE POH POT PYE PHO
RIT ROC ROE ROT RHO TOE TOP TOR TOY TYE YET

CHOP COIR COPY COTE CROP EYOT HYPO PHOT POET PORT POTE PYET PYOT RIOT
RITE ROCH ROPY ROTE TIRO TORC TORI TRIO TROY TYPO YETI

CHOIR PHYTO PORCH PORTE PORTY TORCH

HYPOCRITE

TOTAL 60

165

Average 57   Brainbox 91

AID AIN APE ARE ASP DAG DAN DAP DIE DIG DIN EAN EAR ERA GAD GAE GAN GAP GAR GAS GID GIE GIN IDE NAE NAG NAP NAS PAD PAN PAR PEA PED PER RAD RAG RAN RAP RAS REA RED REP SAD SAE SAG SAI SAN SAP SPA

AGIN AIDE ARED DANG DARE DEAN DEAR DIAN DIER DING GADE GADI GAED GAID GAIN GAPE GARE GASP GIED GNAR IDEA IGAD NAPE NARE NIDE PAID PAIN PANG PARE PEAG PEAN PEAR PRAD RADE RAGI RAID RAIN RANG RANI RAPE RASP READ REAN REAP REIN REOS SAID SAIN SANG SNAG SNAP SNAR SNIG SPAE SPAN SPAR SPED

AIDER ASPER DEIGN DINAR GAPED GAPER PARED PERAI PRANG RAPED REDAN REDIA REIGN REINS SNARE SNIDE SPADE SPAER SPAIN SPANG SPARE SPEAN SPEAR

DIAPER GASPER RASPED REPAID SPARED SPRAID SPRAIN SPRANG SPREAD

READING

SPREADING

TOTAL 140

166

Average 56   Brainbox 96

ACE ALE ARE ART ATE CAR CAT CAW CEE CHA CHE EAR EAT EEL ERA ETA ETH HAE HAT HAW HEL LAC LAH LAR LAT LAW LEA LEE LET RAH RAT RAW REE RET TAE TAR TAW TEA TEE TEL THE WAE WAR WAT

ACHE ALEE ARET CARE CART CATE CHAL CHAR CHAT CHAW EACH EATH ETHE HAET HALE HARE HART HATE HEAL HEAR HEAT HEEL HELE LACE LAER LARE LATE LATH LEAR LEAT LECH LEER LEET RACE RACH RALE RATE RATH REAL REEL TACE TACH TAEL TALE TARE TEAL TEAR TEEL TELA THAW THAE THAR THEA THEE TREE TWAE TWAL WALE WARE WART WATE WHAT

ALERT ARTEL CARET CARTE CATER CHARE CHART CHEAT CHEER CHELA EARTH EATER EATHE ELATE ETHAL HATER HEART LATER LATHE LEACH LEARE LEEAR LEECH LETHE RACHE RATEL RATHE REACH REECH TACHE TEACH TELAE THECA TRACE WALER WATER WHALE WHARE WHEAT WHEEL

AWHEEL CARTEL ECARTE ELATER HEALER HEATER HECATE LATHEE RELATH RELACE THALER THECAE THECAL WHALER

CHEATER RELATHE

CARTWHEEL

TOTAL 163

167

Average 60   Brainbox 98

ALE ALP ALT APE ARE ART ATE EAR EAT ELT ERA ERE ERR ETA LAP LAR LAT LEA LEP PAL PAR PAT PEA PER RAP RAS RAT REP RET SAL SAP SAR SAT TAE TAP TAR TEA

ARET EAST LAER LARE LAST LATE LEAP LEAR LEAT LERE PALE PARE PARR PART PAST PATE PEAL PEAR PEAT PELA PELT PERT PLAT PLEA RALE RAPE RARE RATE RATS REAL REAP REAR SALE SALP SALT SATE SLAE SLAP SLAT STAP STAR TAEL TALE TAPE TARE TEAL TEAR TRAP TSAR

ALERT ALTER APERT ARRET ASTER EASLE EATER ELATE LATER LEARE LEAST PALER PARER PASTE PATER PEART PELTA PLATE PLEAT RAPER RATER REAST REATE SALEP SLATE STALE STARE STARR STEAL STERE TAPER TERAS TERRA TRAPE

EASTER ELATER PALTER PARREL PASTER PELTER PLATER RASTER RELATE REPAST SALTER SLATER STAPLE STARER STEALE STEARE TEARER

PLASTER RELATER STAPLER STEALER

PLASTERER

TOTAL 142